Living
Aunt Lizzie

by Elizabeth Best

illustrated by Greg Gaul

The Characters

Aunt Lizzie

Gertie

Bert

The Setting

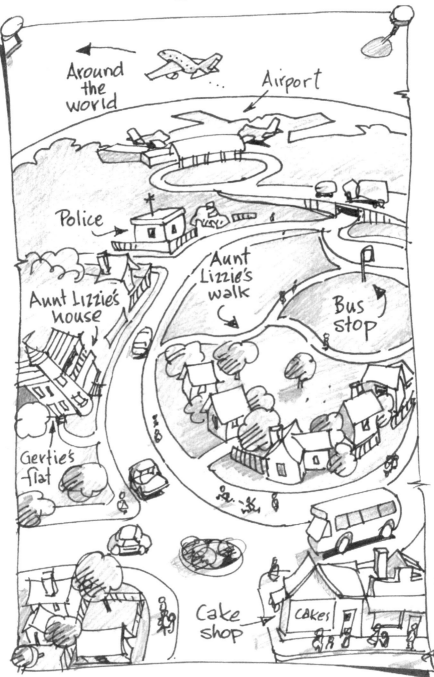

CONTENTS

CHAPTER 1

Happy Birthday

On Aunt Lizzie's 65th birthday,
she was sent a card.

"Happy Birthday," the card said.

On the inside the card said,
"Here's how to live to be 100.
Live to 99 and then be very,
very careful."

"I'll do it!" cried Aunt Lizzie.
"I'll find out how to be very,
very careful!"

She bought a book called
"How To Be Very, Very Careful".

She opened it at page one.
The words filled the page.

"Watch what you eat!"

So she did.

Before eating,
she always put on her glasses.

She ate meat pies
and chocolate cake.
She ate lollies
and sticky buns.
She ate hot chips
and ice-cream.

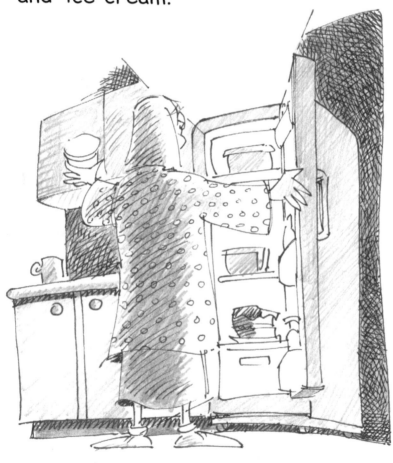

She watched all the food
as it went into her mouth.

Aunt Lizzie thought,
"This is going to be easy."

CHAPTER 2

Fat and Sweet

On page two she read,

"Don't eat too much fat!"

"How much is too much?"
wondered Aunt Lizzie.
She looked at her next meal …
four fat sausages.

"I know," she cried,
"I won't eat four fat sausages.
I'll eat eight thin ones."

9

On page three of the book
there was another rule.

"Don't eat too much sugar!"

Aunt Lizzie's favourite food
was chocolate cake.

Was chocolate cake full of sugar?
She had to find out.

She set off for the cake shop.

The cake shop was full of people.
Aunt Lizzie picked up
a chocolate cake.

She stuck out her tongue
and took a long lick. Yum!

"That's not sugar," she said,
"that's chocolate!"

So she bought five.

Don't Overdo It

On page four of her book she read,

"Walk for an hour a day, but ... DON'T OVERDO IT!"

She tied a meter onto one leg
so she'd know when to stop.
As she walked,
she listened to the meter clicking.
It made her feel good.

"Why didn't I try this before?"
she asked.

Aunt Lizzie walked for an hour.
She didn't turn back.
She just kept going.

Aunt Lizzie was lucky
the first time. After an hour
she stopped at a bus stop.
So she caught the bus home.

The second time,
she went a different way.
She wasn't so lucky.
She had to walk home.

click

"I mustn't overdo it," she thought.
"That's one of the rules."

The next day,
Aunt Lizzie didn't leave the house.
She walked around the bedroom,
up the hall, through the kitchen
and back again. She did this
until the meter told her to stop.

Aunt Lizzie's niece, Gertie, lived
in a little flat under the house.
She heard footsteps and
the meter clicking away like mad.

"Aunt Lizzie," she yelled,
"you've got to stop it. Click, click,
click. Thump, thump, thump.
I can't stand it."

Aunt Lizzie was very upset.
"Don't you want me to live
to be 100?"

CHAPTER 4

Aunt Lizzie Disappears

The next day,
Aunt Lizzie went to the bank
and took out all her money.
She went for a trip
around the world.

One day Gertie said,
"I haven't seen Aunt Lizzie
for months."

Gertie was a little funny
because she ate too much honey.
She'd read that honey was good
for you. But two jars a day
was rather a lot!

Gertie rang her brother Bert.
"Aunt Lizzie's gone," she said.

"We'd better look for her,"
said Bert.

They climbed into his car
and drove around the streets.
They didn't find her.

They looked
in Aunt Lizzie's house.
They put ads in the Daily News.
They talked to the police.
They didn't find Aunt Lizzie.

CHAPTER 5

Not So Careful

The years passed.

One day, Gertie and Bert
were cleaning Aunt Lizzie's house.
They heard the sound of a key
in the lock.

Aunt Lizzie was back.

"Happy Birthday, Auntie!"
they cried. "You're 99 years old!
That book must have helped you.
You must have been very,
very careful."

"Yes," croaked Aunt Lizzie.

As she stepped into the room,
she tripped over the broom.
Aunt Lizzie flung out her arms.

She was going to fall.

But Aunt Lizzie didn't fall.
Her legs gave a skip.
Then she started to dance.
Down the hall and round the kitchen
she danced.

Gertie and Bert ran after her.

Aunt Lizzie made a flying leap
onto a big fat chair.

"You call that being careful?"
they both shouted.

"Oh, I love this old chair,"
Aunt Lizzie said.

Then she laughed. "Aaaahhh,"
she said. "Gertie, you should read
that book of mine.
You'll learn a lot."

Aunt Lizzie tossed the book
onto the table.

Gertie picked up
the well-worn book.
The book fell open to the last page.

Gertie read the big print.

"Have Fun.
Enjoy Your Life."

GLOSSARY

careful
paying lots of attention

croaked
said in a
frog voice

favourite
the most liked

meter
a machine to measure something

tossed
threw

tripped
slipped or stumbled

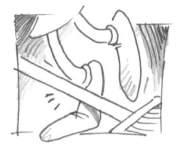

upset
felt sad

wondered
thought about

Elizabeth Best

How high can you jump?

As high as my little Jack Russell dog. She loves darting between my legs and if I don't jump over her, I'm likely to land on the ground with a thud.

Why do ants have 6 legs?

Because they're not spiders — they're ants.

What is your favourite toy?

An enormous stuffed tiger which looks really fierce so I pretend it protects me from burglars.

What is the hardest part of your day?

Getting up in the morning. I'm a night person.

Greg Gaul

How high can you jump?

I have trouble getting off the ground.

Why do ants have 6 legs?

So they can walk.

What is your favourite toy?

I got a cardboard cut-out dinosaur for Christmas. It's called Deinonychus and I'm halfway through making it.

What is the hardest part of your day?

Trying to stay awake after lunch.